A Newfoundland Year

written and illustrated by

Dawn Baker

Pennywell Books
St. John's, NL

Library and Archives Canada Cataloguing in Publication

Baker, Dawn, 1962-, author, illustrator
    A Newfoundland year / artwork and limericks by Dawn Baker.

Originally published: Gander, NL : Art Work Studio, 2008.
Issued in print and electronic formats.
ISBN 978-1-77117-288-2 (pbk.).--ISBN 978-1-77117-178-6 (pdf)

    I. Title.

PS8603.A453N48 2013   jC811'.6   C2013-902541-3
                                                                     C2013-902542-1

PRINTED IN CANADA

This paper has been certified to meet the environmental and social standards of the Forest Stewardship Council® (FSC®) and comes from responsibly managed forests, and verified recycled sources.

Pennywell Books is an imprint of Flanker Press Limited.

FLANKER PRESS LTD.
PO BOX 2522, STATION C
ST. JOHN'S, NL A1C 6K1 CANADA

TELEPHONE: (709) 739-4477   TOLL-FREE: 1-866-739-4420   FAX: (709) 739-4420

WWW.FLANKERPRESS.COM

18 17 16 15 14 13   1 2 3 4 5 6 7 8 9

Cover Design: Peter Hanes

We acknowledge the financial support of the Government of Canada through the Book Publishing Industry Development Program (BPIDP) for our publishing activities; the Canada Council for the Arts, which last year invested $157 million to bring the arts to Canadians throughout the country; the Government of Newfoundland and Labrador, Department of Tourism, Culture and Recreation.

**For Mom and Dad,
Bretta and Mae Brown**

Note: Any words or phrases in this book that are in *italics* may be found in the glossary in the back.

Come take a journey with me,
Through a beautiful land by the sea,
Where there's always good cheer,
Every month of the year,
And on that we will surely agree!

January

The new year has just begun,
It's so cold but we still can have fun,

Our snowmobile's ready,
It rides really steady,
And the **_T'Railway's_** a great place for a run.

February

My **double-ball mitts** are trying,
To keep my fingers from crying,
If you give me a kiss,
I promise you this,
I'll feel warmer and that's no lying.

March

The snow just keeps on falling,
There's no reason to find that appalling,
Out on skis we'll go,
Or snowshoes, you know,
The beautiful outdoors is calling.

April

The ice is now disappearing,
And the slush in our driveway needs clearing,
But mom's cooking *Jigg's Dinner*,
That's always a winner,
And is that a robin I'm hearing?

May

The daffodils out by Pop's fence,
Are sending out pretty good scents,
It's May twenty-fourth,
We're all set to go forth,
In trailers and campers and tents.

June

Finally, the kids are out of school,
No more homework for months, as a rule,
With lobsters in the pot,
The sun shining quite hot,
A day at the beach will be cool.

Head to Newtown or Trinity, don't wait!
Or go visit quaint Twillingate,
An iceberg or whale,
Or someone setting sail,
Will a beautiful memory create.

August

It's Wednesday on Quidi Vidi Lake,
Rowers have months of training at stake,
The **Regatta** has begun,
It's a day of great fun,
The championship each team tries to take.

September

Bakeapples and berries of blue,
Raspberries and partridge berries too,

Is it jam or jelly,
You like in your belly?
Either way, we've got picking to do.

October

The ghouls and the ghosts in great number,
Are out when they usually slumber,
Purity Peppermint Nobs and Kisses,
For all the little misters and misses,
Up the street and down again, they lumber.

It's the night we remember *Guy Fawkes*,
And our parents are watching like hawks,
To see our desire,
For the biggest bonfire,
Is kept safely out on the rocks.

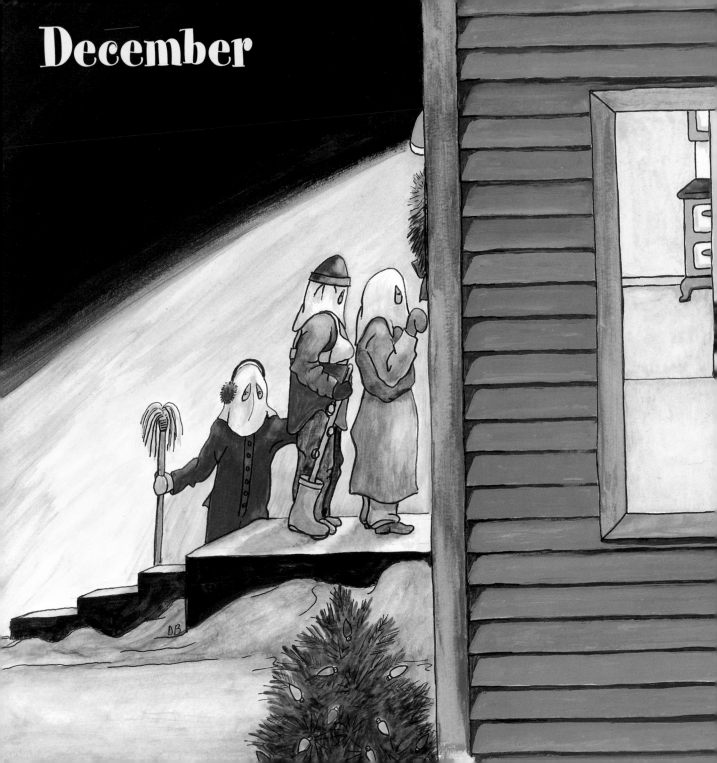

December

Another year winds down and ends,
Still, we're surrounded by all of our friends,
The **mummers** are here,
And all those we hold dear,
And to you, "Best wishes," each one sends.

GLOSSARY

Bakeapples - These are very popular berries that grow on barrens throughout the island portion of Newfoundland and even more abundantly in Labrador. They are similar in appearance to large, orange-yellow raspberries but produce only one berry per plant.

Double-ball mitts - The heavy, handmade mittens created by knitting with two balls of different coloured wool are very warm and durable. Also, the designs created by the two colours are intricate and very beautiful.

Guy Fawkes - The fifth of November is an annual celebration of the foiling of the Gunpowder Plot on that day back in 1605. At that time, Guy Fawkes attempted to blow up the House of Parliament in London, England. Avoiding that disaster is still remembered in Newfoundland and Labrador each year by the lighting of bonfires.

Jiggs Dinner - A traditional meal consisting of salt meat boiled with cabbage, carrots, potatoes and turnips. It is often served with pease pudding and mustard pickles.

Mummers - In Newfoundland and Labrador, there is a two-hundred year long tradition of mummering or janneying between Christmas Day and January sixth, which is known as Old Christmas Day. In complete disguise, the mummers go from house to house to entertain, eat and have fun.

Purity Peppermint Nobs and Kisses - Peppermint Nobs, and candy Kisses of several flavours, including peanut butter, butterscotch and molasses, are delicious candy treats that have been produced for generations by Purity Factories in St. John's. They are just as popular today as ever.

Regatta - The Royal St. John's Regatta is an historic boat racing extravaganza which is held each year on the first Wednesday of August. It is the oldest continuous sporting event in North America with documented proof of races dating back to 1826.

T'Railway - The Newfoundland T'Railway is an unusual Provincial Park which consists of a trail that follows the former route of the Canadian National Railway. (It was The Newfoundland Railway before Confederation with Canada in 1949.) It crosses the island portion of the province from Port aux Basques to St. John's, including running adjacent to the Gander Airport.